FRED BASSET YEARBOOK 2015

Summersdale Publishers Ltd
46 West Street
Chichester
West Sussex
PO19 1RP
UK

www.summersdale.com

Printed and bound in the Czech Republic

ISBN: 978-1-84953-639-4

Substantial discounts on bulk quantities of Summersdale books are available to corporations, professional associations and other organisations.
For details contact Nicky Douglas by telephone: +44 (0) 1243 756902, fax: +44 (0) 1243 786300 or email: nicky@summersdale.com.

Read...

Learn...

Inwardly digest!

We are here to share your load, Yorky. That's what friends are for

Jock and I both feel that you have taken on more than you can chew—

I'm not going in!

I know what curiosity did to the cat!

A lovely day for a stroll—

If you happen to be a St Bernard!

YOU SAID YOU'D GIVE ME A HAND WITH THE WASHING UP, DEAR!

YEP—COMING...

BING BANG BOOM

Don't hold your breath!

Ooops — We've been caught trespassing, lads —

And we can't pull the wool over *his* eyes!

Something isn't right, lads...

I have a strange sinking feeling...

LOOK FRED—A RABBIT!

We bassets aren't known for our lightning reactions!

THIS LOOKS LOVELY, DEAR—YOU HAVE BEEN BUSY!

Straight out of a packet and into the microwave actually—

But we're keeping mum!!

MMM...

Uh-oh! It's those new lads from Tinkers Lane!

I am definitely not playing with them!

They're not called Ruff and Tumble for nothing!

YAPPY YAP

YIPPY YAP

WHAT HAVE YOU GOT THERE, FRED?

Just a little something for your birthday—

RESERVED

I'm spending the evening with my nearest and dearest—

Jock, Yorky—Check!

Bruce, Taffy—Check!

We're good to go!

DO WE HAVE ANY SPIRITS IN THE CUPBOARD, DEAR?

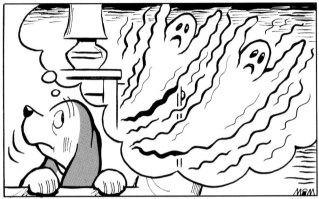

This is rather catching!

NOW, NOW, CHILDREN—QUIET, PLEASE!

DAVID AND JAMES—STOP YOUR TALKING!

SALESBRIDGE PRIMARY SCHOOL

ALICE AND LUCY—GET ON WITH YOUR WORK!

The chattering classes!

Your mission is to infiltrate the Grosvenor Avenue Gang and to seek and retrieve our stolen bones!

And let me remind you, troops—

Failure is not an option!

DINNER, FRED!

WELL, HOW WAS THAT, THEN?

Done to perfection!

YAWN

You'll have to excuse me...

I'm feeling rather lackadaisical today!

OH LOOK—THEY'RE FILMING IN THE HIGH STREET!

Come on—

They may need some extras!

SEE YOU LATER, FRED!

Alert! Alert!

Wardrobe malfunction!